FAMINE

ARTHUR McKEOWN

ILLUSTRATED BY
JOSIP LIZATOVIC

POOLBEG
FOR CHILDREN

For Jane and Andrew, again
AM

For my nephews and niece
JL

Published 1997
by Poolbeg Press Ltd
123 Baldoyle Industrial Estate
Dublin 13, Ireland

Text © Arthur McKeown 1997
Illustrations © Josip Lizatovic 1997

A catalogue record for this book is available from the British Library.

ISBN 1 85371 505 0

Designed by Poolbeg Group Services Ltd
Set by Poolbeg Group Services Ltd in Times 14/22
Printed by ColourBooks Ltd,
Baldoyle, Ireland.

CONTENTS

ABOUT THE AUTHOR

Arthur McKeown lives and works in Belfast. He was educated at Roughfort School, at "Inst" in Belfast and the University of Edinburgh. His books for Poolbeg include *Titanic* and *Robin Hood of the Cave Hill.*

ABOUT THE ILLUSTRATOR

Josip Lizatovic is an award-winning artist who was born in Croatia in 1963. He attended the Academy of Fine Arts in Zagreb University and the Sir John Cass School of Art in London. He is a freelance illustrator and graphic designer. He has won the Sheffield's Children's Award for best illustrated book. Josip Lizatovic lives and works in Dublin.

PLANTING POTATOES

It was daffodil time in County Antrim. The sun was rising over the hills near Belfast. The sky was blue. Birds were starting to sing. It was early in the morning on Joe Campbell's farm, more than one-hundred-and-fifty years ago.

Joe lived with his daughter Maggie near Ballymore. His wife, Mary, had died three years earlier, when Maggie was only five years old.

Joe and his daughter were happy and had a comfortable life on the farm.

In the summer Joe worked in his fields, growing potatoes and other vegetables. He kept a cow and a few pigs. Maggie looked after some chickens in the yard.

In the winter Joe worked at his loom. The steady clattering noise filled the house as he worked. He made linen cloth which he sold in the market in Ballymena. In the old days he earned good money for his work. Now the price was not so high. Lots of people preferred to buy English cotton because it was cheaper.

Today was one of the most important days of the year. It was potato planting day.

"Come on, Maggie!" Joe called. "It's time to plant the potatoes!"

Joe and Maggie went out into the field. Joe carried the sprouting seed potatoes in a big basket. Sal, Maggie's little black-and-white dog, ran along beside her.

Weeks before Joe had dug over the soil in the potato field to get it ready for the new crop. Now he bent over and set each seed potato carefully in the ground. Maggie came behind, covering them with earth and patting them down. The soil was damp and cold, soon their hands were cold too, but they worked on steadily.

"These potatoes will grow strong and healthy," said Joe as they worked in the field.

Sal lay near the hedge, keeping out of the sharp wind.

Joe and Maggie worked hard all day. By evening they were tired and hungry.

"Potato planting is hard work," said Joe. "We've done well today, Maggie. Now it's time to go back home and rest."

THE ROT

In September the potatoes were nearly ready for harvesting. The weather was warm and dry.

One morning Joe went to the market in Ballymena. He was whistling happily as he walked down the lane.

When he returned in the evening he looked worried. He came into the kitchen and threw his cap down on the table.

"What's wrong?" asked Maggie.

"It's the potatoes," said Joe. "While I was in Ballymena I met a man from the Sperrin Mountains. He told me his potatoes were rotting in the fields. Just a week ago his plants seemed strong and healthy. Suddenly one evening there was a terrible stink. Now his plants are dead or dying."

"What about our potatoes?" Maggie asked. "Do you think our potatoes are clean and healthy?"

"I don't know, Maggie," said her father. "I'll go and look." He got up slowly and went out into the yard.

Maggie followed her father into the potato field. Sal came too.

Joe went to the edge of the field and lifted the pitch-fork high over his shoulder and dug deep into the ground. He pulled up a potato plant. The leaves were rich and green, but when he looked closely, Joe saw yellow marks. A few rotting potatoes hung, brown and soggy, on thin white roots.

Joe dropped the plant on the ground. The small, brown potatoes scattered in front of his boots. Then he took the biggest potato and broke it in two. Inside it was brown and rotten.

"Our potatoes are rotten," he said quietly, staring at the potato. Joe sat down on the ground, the potato plant still in his hand, while Maggie and Sal looked on helplessly.

8

FAMINE

The winter of 1845 was hard in Ireland. Many people did not get enough to eat because their potatoes were rotten. Even the animals could not eat them.

In 1846 things got much worse. The farmers did not have enough seed potatoes to plant because they had used them to feed their families. The winter was the longest and coldest anyone could remember. Snow fell and lay for weeks in the fields. The wind blew fiercely day after day.

9

Many people went to work on new roads which were being built in the countryside. The pay was low and they had to work hard even when the weather was very bad.

People died of hunger in many parts of Ireland. The famine was worst in the south and west of the country, especially in Cork and Mayo. People in every county suffered in different ways. A lot of people started to die of disease in the towns and cities.

Maggie and her father saw families of beggars walking the roads around Ballymore. Maggie had never seen people who looked so strange and terrible.

Joe gave what he could to any family that passed along the road near their farm – a few old potatoes in a bucket, or a few cabbages, or a bit of bread. It was not much, but it was all he had to give.

Joe and Maggie were better off than many people in Ireland. Joe had always grown a few vegetables, so they could eat cabbages and turnips.

One morning Joe took their cow to the market in Ballymena. When he came home he put the money in a metal box which he kept hidden under his loom.

"That's our savings," he said. "I think we're going to need all the money we can get if this famine doesn't end soon."

LEAVING BALLYMORE

By the beginning of 1847 people in almost every part of Ireland were suffering terribly.

One evening Joe spoke to his daughter.

"Maggie, we can't stay here," he said. "This winter has been awful. People are dying of hunger. The beggars in the towns have terrible diseases which are killing even more people than the famine. The workhouses are full. Who knows if this great hunger will ever end."

"What can we do?" asked Maggie. "Everywhere is just as bad as Ballymore. Things are bad in Belfast, too."

"We must go much further than Belfast," said her father. "We must go to America."

"America!" exclaimed Maggie, her eyes open wide in surprise.

"We can't stay in Ireland," said Joe sadly. "I can't get money for my weaving. Soon we'll have nothing to eat. We must go while we still can. America is a marvellous place. My uncle went to Virginia when he was a young man. We can go to him and his family."

"Where will we live?" asked Maggie.

"We'll buy a farm. We'll have a good life there, don't worry," said Joe, trying to comfort his daughter.

Maggie looked at the fire in the hearth. After a while she broke the silence.

"You're right," she said. She knew her father had made up his mind. "But it will be hard to leave the only place I've ever known."

"Yes, it will be hard," said her father. "We don't have much money. But it will get us across the Atlantic."

PREPARING FOR THE JOURNEY

It did not take Joe and Maggie long to prepare for their great journey. Joe settled the lease on the farm. He sold the loom he had worked on all his life, but he did not get much money for it. Then he went to the shipping agent in Antrim.

"America it is, Mr Campbell!" said Mr Nichol. "You'll travel on the *Electra* with Captain Mills. She's a clean and tidy ship, with lots of food and water for all the passengers. You'll be glad you chose to cross on the *Electra*."

The afternoon before Joe and Maggie left Ballymore they went for a walk along the shores of Lough Neagh. Sal came too. A few long-necked geese and ducks flew low over their heads and out across the water. Soon the sun would go down behind the hills.

They walked slowly along the water's edge. Then they sat down and looked across to the Sperrin Mountains. The only sound was the water as it lapped gently against the stones.

WALKING TO BELFAST

The sky was grey and misty when Joe and Maggie set off for Belfast. It was early in the morning. Both wore thick coats. Joe carried his walking stick and had a strong canvas sack on his back. In it he had a big, black Bible his father and grandfather had owned.

Maggie had a leather bag with a few warm clothes in it. They both had some bread and fruit to eat on their long journey. Sal came too, with her head high in the air.

They headed down the lane and through the village of Ballymore and walked till they came to the pump in the main street in Antrim. They stopped to drink some water and then continued.

At Tobergill they turned on to the old coach road and began
to walk over the hill towards Belfast. When they reached
the crest of the hill they could see the town far below them.
There were lots of factories with tall chimneys. They could
see the houses where the factory workers lived. At the end
of the lough they saw ships in the port. Far to the south
they could see the Mountains of Mourne.

Joe and Maggie walked down over the green grassy slopes of Ardoyne. As they got closer to the town Joe and Maggie passed ruined houses, with broken doors and windows. They saw lots of miserable women and children, clad in dirty clothes. Maggie had never seen such poverty before.

Outside the Fever Hospital they came upon a crowd of men, women and children, dressed in rags. They looked thin and cold.

"This is where the sick and dying come for help," said Joe. "But no one can help them. Very few will ever come out of the hospital again."

THE DOCKS

Joe and Maggie walked along the narrow cobbled streets leading to the docks. Joe had only been in Belfast a few times. He did not like the crowds and the smells.

As they neared the docks they passed in front of the houses of the rich Belfast merchants who used to live there. Most of the houses were closed and boarded up.

Maggie loved all the activity. The streets were noisy and crowded. She had never seen so many people.

As they walked around the harbour they saw passengers getting ready for their long sea journey. Some had boxes and others had sacks. Others had only small bundles on their backs.

"Are all these people coming on our ship?" Maggie asked her father.

"No, they're not, Maggie," said Joe, smiling for the first time in many days. "But I'm sure the *Electra* will be crowded enough."

Joe carried his bag over his shoulder. It felt a lot heavier after the long walk from Ballymore. Joe and Maggie were both exhausted and their long voyage across the Atlantic had not even started yet.

THE ELECTRA

"Let's find the *Electra*," said Joe. "It must be along the docks somewhere."

They walked along the quay, looking carefully at each ship.

At last they found the *Electra*. Two sailors were busy lowering the gang plank on to the quay.

"Can we come aboard?" called Joe. "We've booked our crossing to America. Our name's Campbell. I've got our tickets here."

He waved the two tickets he had bought in Antrim, but the two sailors kept working and said nothing.

A few moments later the captain appeared. He was a short, fat man with long, greasy hair and a grey beard.

"I'm Captain Mills of the *Electra*," he shouted. "Come aboard now. You'll get good places. But first let me see those tickets of yours. They'd better be in order or you'll be staying in Ireland!"

He laughed at his own joke. Then he looked closely at the two tickets.

"They'll do," said Captain Mills at last.

Joe and Maggie started to go up the gang plank, with Sal close at Joe's heels.

"No dogs!" shouted Captain Mills. "We can't have animals on board. You'll have to leave your dog behind."

Maggie stopped and looked at her father.

"We'll have to leave Sal behind," said Joe quietly.

There were tears in Maggie's eyes as Joe chased Sal back along the gang plank.

"Come on, Sal," he said. "Let's find someone to look after you." They walked back along the quay, Maggie following behind.

Joe went up to an old woman who was sitting outside her shop. She had a few loaves of bread for sale.

"This wee dog will be a good friend for you. Will you look after her?" he asked.

Sal wagged her tail and lay down near the old woman. "I'll look after her," she said to Joe. Maggie wrapped her arms around Sal's neck and kissed the little dog goodbye.

Joe and Maggie walked slowly back to the *Electra* and boarded the ship.

Captain Mills came forward.

"Where do we have to go?" asked Joe.

"Down below the deck," said Captain Mills, pointing at a narrow hole in the deck. "The rest of the passengers won't be as lucky as you. The ship will soon be crowded and noisy. We still have a lot of cargo to bring on board."

Maggie and her father went down a narrow ladder and sat in a corner. It was damp and dark. Joe lay down to rest using his sack as a pillow. Maggie sat quietly beside her father.

They were thinking about America.

CROSSING THE ATLANTIC

Early in the morning the *Electra* was ready for sea. It was 15 May, 1847. Maggie watched the sailors as they untied the great ropes which bound the ship to the shore.

The ship was crowded. Not many of the passengers knew anyone else, but they soon made friends with each other.

Maggie and her father stayed on deck as long as they could. They watched as they passed Carrickfergus with its great castle. The passengers spent most of the day looking at the coast of Antrim, Derry and Donegal. Then the *Electra* headed out to sea. A mist came down. Ireland was hidden for ever.

"We're on our way," Joe said to his daughter. "Ireland's behind us now."

The *Electra* was alone on the open sea, with no land ahead until they reached America.

Life on board the ship soon became monotonous.

To pass the time, Joe and Maggie talked to their fellow passengers and listened to stories about the famine in other parts of Ireland.

One man from Cork described how bad the famine was in the south: "I saw hundreds of people dying on the sides of the roads. I saw people eating nettles, raw and stinging. I saw an old man lying dead in a ditch with bits of grass sticking out of his mouth."

Another passenger described his experience in Mayo: "Our neighbour was evicted for using some corn to feed his starving children. I heard about several other evictions, too. In one village a poor farmer and his family had to watch as the landlord's men destroyed his house."

"Where I come from," said a third passenger, "people had to steal to stay alive. I even heard of people committing crimes, burning crops or stealing animals, in the hope that the police would arrest them and send them to prison. At least prisoner's get fed!"

JOURNEY'S END

Life on board the *Electra* was hard. Joe and Maggie tried to spend as much time as possible in the fresh air, wearing their heavy coats to keep out the cold winds.

"There's disease below deck, Maggie," said her father. "The air stinks and it's filthy. Let's do our best to keep healthy so we get safely across to the other side."

Each afternoon Joe and Maggie ate some food they had brought with them from Ballymore, but it did not last long. Then they ate the food they got from the crew. The soup was thin and watery.

"This soup won't do us much good," said Joe wearily. "There's no meat in it. It's just warm water with a bit of barley and old cabbage leaves."

The passengers got less and less to eat each day. By the end of the journey even the few scraps they had were rotten so that no one could bear to eat them.

The water for drinking was mouldy. No one could keep clean.

A few of the passengers were near death, exhausted after
all they had suffered during the long voyage. Some
caught a fever. They lay below the deck of the ship
coughing loudly. Many old people died during the long
journey. There were no doctors on board the ship.

AMERICA!

At last, nearly eight weeks after the *Electra* left Belfast, the long journey was nearing an end.

One day, late in the afternoon, sea birds appeared.

"Birds!" shouted one of the crew standing at the side of the deck. "I can see birds!"

"We can't be far from land now!" shouted another man.

Far out to sea, high over the water, a few gulls were circling in the blue sky above a shoal of fish. Now and again one of the birds dived into the sea, emerging with a fish in its beak.

The next day one of the passengers spotted seaweed.

"Look! Seaweed!" he shouted, pointing into the water. "Surely it can't be much further now?"

All the passengers were excited.

"We must be nearly there," they said over and over again.

It was several more days before the *Electra* moved into the great mouth of the Hudson River. For the first time in weeks the passengers had fresh water to drink.

"We're there!" said Joe happily. "We've crossed the Atlantic safely. God has answered all our prayers."

As other passengers cheered and shouted, Joe and Maggie bowed their heads and thanked God for bringing them safely across the wide ocean. They were ready to start their new lives in America.

A NEW LIFE

Maggie and her father arrived in New York in July 1847. They were exhausted after their long journey. Some passengers could hardly walk.

Joe and Maggie left New York and went to the rich farmlands in the south-west. They settled near Charleston in West Virginia, not far from Joe's uncle and his family.

Joe bought some land with the money he had brought from Ireland. He became a farmer again.

When Maggie grew up she married a man called Paul
Kelly whose family had come from County Antrim
many years before the famine. Maggie and Paul had two
sons and a daughter.

Joe often came to visit Maggie and his grandchildren in their new home and helped Paul with the work around the farm.

When he was an old man Joe gave his farm to Maggie and moved in with his daughter and her family.

One evening, many years after their arrival in America, Maggie was sitting alone in the kitchen with her father. He was over eighty years old. He walked using the stick he had brought from Ballymore.

Paul was still out in the yard, finishing off some chores. The children were in bed.

Maggie was sitting in a rocking chair, sewing a dress for her daughter, Mary. Mary's little dog, Sal, was asleep in her basket beside the fire.

The clock was ticking quietly in the warm farm kitchen.

Joe broke the silence.

"It's a long way from Ballymore, Maggie," he said
quietly. "I'm glad we made the decision to come here all
those years ago."

"Yes, I'm glad we came, too," Maggie replied. "It was a
hard journey but we have a good life here."

Joe closed his eyes and fell asleep while Maggie continued her work on Mary's dress.

The clock in the kitchen ticked quietly.

There were some yellow flowers in a jar in the middle of the kitchen table.

It was daffodil time in West Virginia.

ALSO BY ARTHUR MCKEOWN

ROBIN HOOD OF THE CAVE HILL

Naoise O'Haughan was a highwayman. He lived at the back of the Cave Hill in Belfast. He stole money from the rich and gave it to the poor. He was Belfast's Robin Hood!

So begins the story of Belfast's famous outlaw of two hundred years ago, a tale full of excitement and danger. *Robin Hood of the Cave Hill* was written specially for independent readers and is delightfully illustrated by Cathy Dineen.

ISBN: 1 85371 264 7

TITANIC

The *Titanic* was built in Belfast. Everyone thought she was the best ship in the world. They thought she would never sink. Then one night she hit an iceberg in the middle of the Atlantic . . .

Join Mary and her mother and father as they board the *Titanic* and begin their voyage to New York on the most luxurious ship of all time. Meet Captain Smith, on his retirement voyage, and Mr Andrews who built the magnificent "unsinkable" ship. Evocatively illustrated by Peter Hogan.

ISBN: 1 85371 516 6

POOLBEG
FOR CHILDREN